WALT TEASER

DOUBLE TROUBLE!

THE BRUISE BROTHERS

Mr. Hill.

LEW STRINGER

Here he is...
Faceache
...the boy with a THOUSAND FACES!

NOW! PAY ATTENTION!

HEY! FACEACHE! I'M MEETING MY UNCLE AFTER SCHOOL TONIGHT! IT'LL BE GREAT!

WHY'S THAT, CYRIL?

HE OWNS A SWEET SHOP AND HE ALWAYS BRINGS ME LOADS OF GOODIES! I'LL SAVE YOU HALF!

WOW! THANKS!

YOU, BOY!

YOU WERE TALKING! YOU'LL STAY BEHIND TONIGHT FOR DETENTION!

B- BUT, SIR, I'M MEETING MY UNCLE AFTER SCHOOL!

TOO BAD! YOU'LL MISS HIM NOW, WON'T YOU?

CRIKEY! THIS COULD COST BOTH OF US OUR SWEETS!

LATER...

CLASS DISMISSED— EXCEPT FOR CYRIL! I'LL BE BACK LATER!

GOOD! NOW'S MY CHANCE!

WHAT CAN I DO? I CAN'T BE IN TWO PLACES AT ONCE!

DON'T BE TOO SURE! WATCH!

WOW! A CYRIL-LOOK-ALIKE- "SCRUNGE"! FANTASTIC!

SCRUNGE!

YOU GET OFF TO SEE YOUR UNCLE! I'LL DO YOUR DETENTION!

ONE HOUR LATER...

RIGHT! YOU CAN GO NOW, CYRIL! I HOPE YOUR UNCLE DEALS WITH YOU WHEN HE LEARNS WHY YOU'RE LATE!

UN-SCRUNGE!

NOW TO FIND THE REAL CYRIL!

SCHOOL EXIT →

AND...

LOOK AT ALL THESE SWEETS, FACEACHE!

WOW! IT WAS WORTH DOING SOME DETENTION FOR THAT LOT!

SWEETS

NEXT DAY...

I TRUST YOU GOT WHAT YOU DESERVED FROM YOUR UNCLE!

NOT HALF, SIR!

HEE, HEE! AND I GOT THE OTHER HALF!

IVOR LOTT and TONY BROKE
with MILLY O'NAIRE and PENNY LESS

I'M SURE IT SAID SOMETHING ABOUT FARMS ON THOSE LORRIES!

AND THEY'VE ALL GONE INTO IVOR'S GROUNDS!

LET'S SEE WHAT'S GOING ON!

AH, RIFF-RAFF! MILLY AND I HAVE STARTED A FARM HERE!

COO!

A FARMHOUSE! I CAN IMAGINE AN OPEN FIRE... HOT, BUTTERED SCONES... BACON AND EGG SIZZLING IN A HUGE, COPPER FRYING PAN...

EH? OLD-FASHIONED NONSENSE!

THIS IS A MODERN FARMHOUSE! THE NERVE-CENTRE OF THE OPERATION!

YIPE! ER...WHERE DO YOU KEEP YOUR TRACTORS, PLOUGHS AND THINGS LIKE THAT?

TUT-TUT! TRACTORS, INDEED! COME AND SEE OUR CROPS GROWING!

AH! WE'RE GOING TO THE FIELDS!

A LOTT MENT LTD.

NO! TO THIS GIGANTIC SHED!

FARM SUPPLIES LTD

FA SUPP LTC

AND...

THE CONVEYOR BELT IS FILLED WITH RICH, GROWING MIXTURE! FIRST, I PRESS THE BUTTON THAT ALLOWS SEEDS TO TRICKLE ON TO IT!

SEED FLOW

SEEDS NEED MOISTURE AND WARMTH, SO THE BELT MOVES SLOWLY ALONG TO GIVE THEM BOTH!

NOW WE GO UPSTAIRS TO ANOTHER PART OF THE SAME BELT, AND SEE THAT THE CROP IS GROWING NICELY!

HEAT!

THEN, HERE AT THE TOP OF THE BUILDING, WE SEE WHERE THE RIPE GRAIN IS HARVESTED! BUT WE'RE NOT FINISHED YET!

CUT!

WHIRRRR!

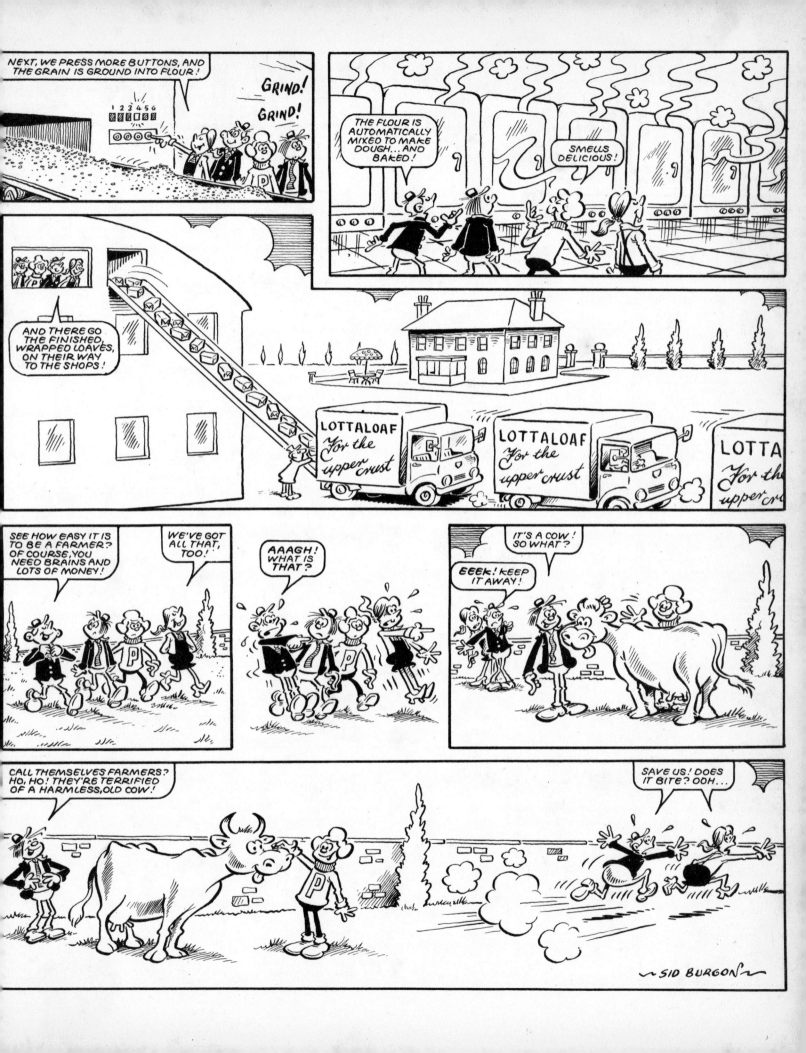

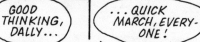

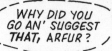

TEST YOURSELF

Can you stand up for yourself?

To find out, answer each of the questions, tick the appropriate one, then check your score, pals!

1 The crowded school bus arrives and several rough kids push in front of you, trying to take the last places. Do you. . .
A. Barge your way through the queue-jumpers?
B. Protest quietly to the bus conductor?
C. Wait for the next bus, even though you'll be late?

2 Some classmates are larking about, and when Teach arrives he gives **you** 500 lines, as well as the troublemakers. Do you. . .
A. Ask your mates to explain that you weren't doing anything?
B. Wait until you get home, and ask Mum to write a note to Sir?
C. Politely but firmly tell Teach he has made a mistake?

3 At the busy chip shop, you're given a bag containing a too-small portion of chips. Do you. . .
A. Trudge off, telling yourself that chips are fattening, anyway?
B. Ask for more and, if unsuccessful, demand your money back?
C. Complain, but give up when the people in the queue tell you to stop holding them up?

4 Your pals want you to go to the park, but you want to go home and revise for the big test coming up. Do you. . .
A. Explain, and ignore their scoffing and jeering?
B. Pretend you've got to visit the doctor?
C. Go along, 'cos that's easier than making excuses?

TURN THE PAGE TO CHECK YOUR SCORE

15—20
You're no pushover, and never hesitate to air your feelings! But it's sometimes better to give in than get into a scrap!

6—14
If you're pushed too far you'll protest, but only if there are some mates, or Mum, around to support you!

0—5
You hate attention focused on you so you keep quiet, even when unfairly treated. You'll probably grow up to umpire a McEnroe match!

1. A—5, B—3, C—0; 2. A—2, B—0, C—5; 3. A—0, B—5, C—3; 4. A—5, B—2, C—0.

SCHOOL BELLE

SCHOOL TEAM

MUMMY'S BOY

YOUNG ARFUR

BETTER GET A MOVE ON, ARFUR! IT'S NEARLY NINE AN' WE'VE A SPELLIN' TEST FIRST THING WITH MR. NAGG!

'OLD ON A SEC, TERRY...

HATE SKOOL

... OL' NAGG WENT 'OME EARLY YESTERDAY WITH SPOTTYITIS, REMEMBER? SO HE'S NOT GOING TO BE IN FOR TODAY'S SPELLIN' TEST, IS HE?

NO, DALLY, HE ISN'T— BUT I AM!

ERK! MR. STRONGMAN!

HATE SKOOL

LOOKS LIKE WE'RE ALL GOIN' TO 'AVE TO DO THE TEST, AFTER ALL, ARFUR!

NOT IF I CAN 'ELP IT, TERRY!

SO...

GET OUT YOUR PENS, BOYS, WHILE I ... GAH! WHO KEEPS YAWNING?

YAWN! SORRY, SIR! YAWN...

... IT'S ME, SIR! YAWN!

HMPH! I SUPPOSE YOU WERE UP HALF THE NIGHT WATCHING THE LATE NIGHT FILM, DALLY!

ER, THE LATE NIGHT FOOTBALL 'IGHLIGHTS, ACTUALLY, SIR!

WELL, IT MUST'VE BEEN ON LATE, BECAUSE I DIDN'T SEE IT!

YOU DON'T KNOW WHAT YOU MISSED, SIR! TWO GOALS IN THE FIRST THREE MINUTES BY GRODDLE OF UNITED!

WHAT? GRODDLE GOT TWO?

YEAH! BUT CITY SOON EQUALISED WITH DOBSON GETTIN' TWO PENALTIES!

GLERK! T-TWO PENALTIES?

MIND YOU, UNITED TOOK THE LEAD AGAIN IN THE SECOND 'ALF— BUT THAT'S ANOTHER STORY!

NEVER MIND, BOY! CARRY ON!

... WAFFLE ... FREE KICK WITH FIFTEEN MINUTES TO GO ... BLAH ... CORNER KICK ... BLAH!

HEH, HEH! ARFUR'S GOT SIR 'SPELL'-BOUND!

AN' WITH TWO MINUTES 'TIL BREAK, WE'RE 'BOUND' TO MISS OUR 'SPELLING' TEST!

DREDGE

M°Hill.

Here he is...
Faceache
...the boy with a THOUSAND FACES!

HERE'S OLD SNIPE ON THE PROWL! I BET HE'S AFTER MY MATHS HOMEWORK!

BUT IT'S NOT DUE UNTIL AFTER LUNCH!

YES! BUT HE'S ALREADY GOT EVERYBODY ELSE'S!

FACEACHE. COME BACK!

WAIT! HAVEN'T YOU FORGOTTEN SOMETHING?

I KNEW IT! I'LL MAKE A RUN FOR IT!

COME HERE, YOU STUPID BOY!

OH, NO! HE'S CHASING AFTER ME!

STOP! STOP!

POUND! POUND!

GASP! PANT! HE'S GAINING ON ME! I'D BETTER "SCRUNGE" MY WAY OUT OT THIS ONE!

HERE GOES!

SCRUNGE!

YOU, BOY! DID YOU SEE FACEACHE GO PAST?

ER... NO, SIR!

ARE YOU SURE? I NEED TO GET HOLD OF HIM VERY QUICKLY!

ER, I SAW HIM THIS MORNING, AND HE SAID HIS HOMEWORK W-WOULD DEFINITELY BE IN AFTER L-LUNCH, SIR!

GOOD! BUT THAT'S NOT WHY I WANTED HIM!

OH?

HE LEFT HIS CREAM CAKE IN THE DINING-ROOM - BUT I'LL NEVER FIND HIM NOW, SO I'LL EAT IT!

HUH?

IF YOU SEE HIM, CHOMP, TELL HIM HIS CAKE WAS SUPERB!

GRR! I'LL BET HE WON'T SAY THAT ABOUT MY HOMEWORK, WHEN HE SEES IT!

UN-SCRUNGE!

Good Guy

I WANT YOU TO DO YOUR SUMS TONIGHT, **WITHOUT** USING CALCULATORS! YOU MUST USE YOUR BRAINS!

BACK HOME...

BETTER GET THESE SUMS DONE, I SUPPOSE!

HERE'S YOUR CALCULATOR!

NO! TEACHER SAID NOT TO USE IT!

OUCH! HE REMEMBERED!

I'VE GOT TO THINK OF SOMETHING! GOT TO... THINK... THINK...

AT LAST...

GOT IT... THE PERFECT PLAN!

I'LL PUNCH THOSE NUMBERS INTO IT, AND IF YOU PRESS THE **EQUALS** BUTTON, YOU'LL HAVE THE **ANSWER**!

THESE NUMBERS?

IT'S HAPPENED! GUY'S BEEN BAD!

OKAY!

SEE? NOW I'M PUTTING IN THE NEXT COLUMN OF NUMBERS! GET READY TO PRESS!

THERE!

YIPPEE! YOU'VE DISOBEYED TEACHER... USED THE CALCULATOR FOR HOMEWORK!

NO, I HAVEN'T!

BUT I SAW YOU!

I FINISHED MY HOMEWORK PAGES AGO! I'VE BEEN WORKING OUT CRICKET AVERAGES! THANKS FOR HELPING!

AAGH!

AND...

IT DOESN'T TAKE MUCH TO **CALCULATE** THAT YOU'VE FAILED AGAIN, MISCHIEVOUS MIKE!

TEMPTATION LIMITED

TERRY BAVE

DOUBLE TROUBLE!

DRACULA DOBBS

It's a Nice Life

MUST HAVE A WANDER AROUND MY HEATED GREENHOUSE!

EVEN THIS EARLY IN THE YEAR, IT'S AMAZING WHAT GROWS IN IT'S WARM ATMOSPHERE! SWEET PEAS... TROPICAL PLANTS...

ER - PEOPLE, TOO, OLLIE!

WARM!

ERK! WHAT'RE YOU LOT DOING IN MY GREENHOUSE?

WELL, ACTUALLY, JUST GROWING THE ODD LITTLE PLANT! WE KNEW YOU WOULDN'T MIND!

MIND? OF COURSE I MIND! KINDLY REMOVE ANYTHING WHICH IS YOURS!

ERK! ODD LITTLE PLANT, INDEED! WELL, WHAT A CHEEK!

WELL, OLLIE, YOU WERE HARDLY USING THE PLACE AT ALL!

IT'S MY BUSINESS HOW MUCH I USE IT! BUT I'M NOT HEATING IT FOR YOUR BENEFIT!

WHAT DO WE DO NOW? IF THE PLANTS DON'T GET BACK INTO A GREENHOUSE ATMOSPHERE SOON, THEY'LL DIE!

RIGHT! THEN WE'LL JUST HAVE TO GET OURSELVES A GREENHOUSE!

COLD WIND!

BUT, STAN, WE CAN'T AFFORD A GREENHOUSE!

AH, WE'LL BE ABLE TO AFFORD THE ONE I'M THINKING ABOUT!

I'LL BE GLAD IF YOU TAKE THE OLD WRECK OFF MY HANDS! CAN'T SEE HOW IT WILL BE ANY USE TO YOU, THOUGH!

OH, YOU'LL BE SURPRISED, FARMER WURZEL!

WURZEL FARM

WE ALL WILL BE!

BEASTENDERS

IT'S HALLOWEEN IN ALBERT SCARE...

BETTER BE ON OUR GUARD TONIGHT HERMAN'S BOUND TO HAVE SOMETHING NASTY IN STORE FOR US!

ALBERT SCARE ANGELS H.Q.

AT HERMAN'S H.Q...

IS GRISWALD THE GRUESOME GREEN GOBLIN IN?

NO! HE'S OUT HAUNTING TONIGHT!

MONSTERS H.Q.

RUPERT

BAH! ALL THE MONSTERS ARE BOOKED UP!

IT IS HALLOWEEN, HERMAN! MONSTERS ARE ALWAYS BUSY AT HALLOWEEN.

SO IT IS! I FORGOT ALL ABOUT THAT!

NEVER MIND! THERE MUST BE SOME MONSTERS WHO AREN'T BUSY TONIGHT!

JUST THEN...

WE'RE AVAILABLE!

FOOFF!

! ?

SPLOOSH!

GRR! I WISH THEY WOULDN'T DO THAT! IT ALWAYS SETS OFF THE SMOKE ALARM AND SPRINKLER SYSTEM!

ME AND MY FRIENDS ARE FROM THE "MONSTER AND GHOSTS RETIREMENT HOME!"

SENIOR SPOOKS!?

WE MAY BE OLD, BUT WE CAN STILL SCARE HUMANS!

ER... I'M OVER HERE, YOU SHORT-SIGHTED FIEND!

TAP!

OKAY, I'LL GIVE YOU A TRY!

WHAT DID HE SAY? "HE THINKS IT'LL STAY DRY!"

HERMAN'S H.Q.

LATER...

I W-WONDER W-WHAT G-GHOSTLY GHOULS ARE OUT R-ROAMING THE S-STREETS TONIGHT?

CREAK!

CREAK!

BOOoo

CREAK!

AAAGGGGHHHH!

CONTINUED OVER THE PAGE

HERMAN IS ANGRY...

WE ASK FOR SOME MONSTERS TO HELP US GET RID OF THE HUMANS, AND WHAT DO WE GET?

A BUNCH OF HORROR HAS-BEENS!

ICE CREAMS, DID HE SAY? MAKE MINE A RASPBERRY RIPPLE!

BAH! GET YOURSELVES SORTED OUT OR I'LL BANISH YOU BACK TO THE SPIRIT WORLD BEFORE YOU CAN SAY 'PETRIFIED PENSION BOOKS'!

HERMANS H.Q.

SO...

OPTICIAN

MY MATE NEEDS SOME NEW SPECS!

AAAGGGHHH!

RECEPTION

ASSORTED SPECS

THEY'RE LEAVING. LOOKS LIKE WE'LL HAVE TO SERVE OURSELVES!

READ THAT CHART!

WHAT CHART?

A X COR HELP OOER WWW

TRY THESE! I'VE GLUED THREE PAIRS TOGETHER TO GIVE THEM EXTRA STRENGTH!

PERFECT!

TRIP!

MEANWHILE...

GARAGE

AAAGGGHHH!

YIKES!

GARAGE

ROAR!

NOW MY WHEELS HAVE GOT TURBO-POWER! CACKLE! CACKLE!

AND...

DENTAL LABORATORY

WOW! WHAT A PAIR OF NEAT NASHERS! I'LL TAKE 'EM!

CONTINUED OVER THE PAGE

The Scruffs... **TOP of the CLASS** ...The Toffs

MORNING BREAK...

CYRIL AND HIS FRIENDS ARE IN CHARGE OF THE SCHOOL TUCK SHOP TODAY!

A VERY WISE CHOICE, SIR, IF I MAY SAY SO!

GLARE!

GLOAT!

SMUG!

YOU LOT AREN'T UP TO SUCH A RESPONSIBLE TASK!

WRONG, CYRIL! IT'S YOUR TURN, THAT'S ALL! HERBERT AND HIS FRIENDS WILL GET THEIR CHANCE ANOTHER DAY!

PRANCE! SWAGGER!

NARKED!

HUH! I SUPPOSE WE'LL 'AVE TO BUY STUFF FROM **THEM** OR GO WITHOUT!

TUCK SHOP

OI! THEY'VE KEPT BACK THE GOODIES!

ALL WE'RE BEIN' OFFERED ARE BROKEN BISCUITS!

SNIGGER!

BROKEN BISCUITS! 1P. A PIECE!

UNFAIR!

WHAT'S ALL THE NOISE ABOUT?

RANT!

BELLOW!

THUMP!

Buster

SO...

I SHOULD HAVE KNOWN THERE WOULD BE TROUBLE! OUT!

IN A PADDY 'COS HIS CUPPA'S GETTING COLD!

SHAME!

ARF! WHAT A COME-DOWN! THEY'VE BEEN BANNED FROM RUNNIN' THE TUCK SHOP!

MOCK! HOOT!

TRUDGE!

LEAVE IT TO US, TEACH! **WE'LL** RUN THE PLACE PROPERLY!

MUTTER!

STOMP!

CURRY CHEWS

HAM & JAM CRISPS

RUN IT RIGHT AWAY FROM THEM, THAT IS!

ARF, ARF!

?UFF! C-COME BACK HERE! WE WANT TO SPEND OUR ALLOWANCES!

RATTLE! CLINK!

ZOOM!

THEN...

TUCK SHOP

HOW ARE THINGS GOING NOW, I WONDER... OH, NO!

GIBBER!

LOOK OUT! IT'S TEACH! BRAKES ON!

SCREECH!

THUD!

THUNDER!

PRANG!

IVOR LOTT and TONY BROKE
with MILLY O'NAIRE and PENNY LESS

MIKE'S BIKE

HEY! THERE GOES DAD IN OUR CAR!

WAIT A MINUTE! DAD SAID HE WAS STAYING IN ALL DAY!

AFTER IT, BIKE... IT'S BEEN STOLEN!

ND...

CHOINK!

BRAKES ON! WELL DONE, BIKE, WE'RE SLOWING HIM DOWN!

S-T-R-A-I-N!

SHUDDER!

UH, OH! YOU'VE PULLED OFF THE BUMPER!

YIKES!

JANG!

VROOOOM!

THUMP!

WHAT THE...?

POLICE

GRR! IT'S ALL HIS FAULT!

A641COP

THAT'S MY DAD'S CAR! YOU STOLE IT!

WHAT HAVE YOU GOT TO SAY FOR YOURSELF?

WELL...ER... IF THIS IS HIS ADDRESS...

...HIS DAD ASKED ME TO DELIVER HIS CAR BACK TO HIM!

ULP! SO THAT'S WHY DAD WAS STAYING IN!

POLICE

I'VE SPENT ALL MORNING REPAIRING IT!

GULP! I'LL NEED REPAIRING WHEN DAD FINDS OUT!

X-RAY SPECS

114.

SCHOOL TEAM

Just JOKING

It's a Nice Life

IT'S REALLY HANDY HAVING THIS FOREST ONLY FIVE MILES' WALK FROM HOME!

IT'S REALLY HANDY HAVING THIS FOREST ONLY A FEW MINUTES DRIVE FROM HOME!

HEY! IT'S THE JONESES! WHAT ARE YOU DOING HERE?

IT'S THEM! WHAT ARE YOU DOING HERE?

WE'RE COLLECTING FIREWOOD! AFTER ALL, WE DON'T HAVE GAS OR ELECTRICITY TO COOK BY!

HUH! I'M LOOKING FOR DECORATIVE TWIGS FOR MY FLORAL ART CLASS!

YEEK!

HO, HO! MAKE A WISH, MADDIE!

GRAB!

DOH! I WISH YOU AND YOUR SILLY ANIMAL WERE MILES AWAY!

SNAP!

AW! COME ON NOW, MADDIE! WE'RE NOT THAT BAD!

BOMP!

WE'LL WORK TOGETHER! WE'LL HELP YOU COLLECT LITTLE TWIGS AND YOU CAN HELP US COLLECT FIREWOOD!

HUH! BUT YOU WOULDN'T KNOW WHAT TO LOOK FOR..!

HOW ABOUT THIS ONE, MRS. JONES?

YEEK!

WAAH!

SHE MUST BE JEALOUS BECAUSE WE FOUND IT FIRST!

DON'T BE SILLY! IT'S THAT DISGUSTING SPIDER! IT FRIGHTENED HER!

I BET SHE GAVE THE SPIDER A BIT OF A SHOCK, TOO!

The PARK

IT SAYS HERE THAT JANUARY AND FEBRUARY ARE THE QUIETEST MONTHS IN BRITISH PARKS!

WEEKLY PARKY

BRITISH PARKIES SET NEW SNOOZING RECORDS!

ZZZZ!

WHAT'S THAT?

SQUEAK! SQUEAK!

GROAN! I WISH SOMEBODY WOULD TELL THE GROT STREET GANG THAT IT'S MEANT TO BE QUIET JUST NOW!

SQUEAK!

SQUEAK!

OI, YOU LOT! GET OFF THOSE SQUEAKING BIKES!

WE'RE GETTING OFF, ANYWAY!

MUTTER! PESKY KIDS! STILL, I'VE STOPPED THE NOISE!

PREPARING FOR A KIP!

BUT THEN...

DOH! WHAT NOW?

SQUEAK! SQUEAK!

LEAP!

YOU'VE WOKEN ME UP GOOD AND PROPER NOW WITH ALL THAT SQUEAKING! FOR THAT YOU CAN HELP ME WITH MY WORK!

SQUEAK!

SQUEAK!

SQUEAK!

POOR DECISION, PARKY...

AAGH! STOP!

SQUEAK!

SQUEAK!

SQUEAK!

CREAK!

I CAN'T STAND THAT SQUEAKING! JUST STAND PERFECTLY STILL! DON'T MOVE A MUSCLE!

SIGH...

—TOM PATERSON—

IVOR LOTT and TONY BROKE

with MILLY O'NAIRE and PENNY LESS

OUR BARBECUE MAY NOT BE VERY POSH, BUT I BET THE SAUSAGES TASTE GOOD WHEN THEY'RE COOKED!

BUT...

OH, NO! THEY'VE CAUGHT FIRE!

I HAD THIS NEARBY, JUST IN CASE!

OH, DEAR! THAT'S PUT AN END TO THAT!

AW, HAW-HAW! POSH PEOPLE LIKE SMOKED SALMON—RIFF-RAFF SEEM TO LIKE SMOKY, BURNED SAUSAGES!

GROAN! IVOR AND MILLY! TRUST THEM TO TURN UP AT THE WRONG MOMENT!

COME AND SEE OUR BARBECUE! EVERYTHING IS BIGGER AND BETTER—NATURALLY!

WE MAY AS WELL, PENNY! WE MIGHT EVEN PICK UP SOME TIPS!

LOTT HALL

WHAT'S BEING BUILT THERE? A NEW GARAGE FOR ALL YOUR CARS?

OH, DEARIE-ME, NO!

IT'S OUR BARBECUE SITE! ONE HAS TO DO IT PROPERLY, OF COURSE!

BARBECUE!

SOON...

SO NOW IT'S TIME TO EAT!

OH, DEARIE-ME, NO! WE HAVEN'T EVEN DECIDED ON THE FUEL TO USE!

WE WANT THE ONE WITH THE HOTTEST FLAME!

TEST 1   TEST 2   TEST 3   TEST 4

COKE   COAL   CHARCOAL   GAS

WONDER WELLIES

Rodney & DEZ

RIGHT, MISSUS! LOVELY GARDEN GNOMES TO BRIGHTEN UP YOUR LIFE!

ER...NO THANKS!

HE LOOKS A REAL LITTLE SHARK!

NO, TA!

I'M IN A HURRY!

HMM...SOME-TIMES IT DOESN'T PAY TO LOOK TOO SHARP AND COOL!

THIS JOB NEEDS SOMEONE WITH AN HONEST FACE, AND THICK WITH IT...ROD-NEEE!

HAVE A GO! THERE'LL BE 50 PER CENT COMMISSION IN IT FOR YOU!

WELL, I DON'T KNOW IF I'LL BE ANY GOOD AT THIS...

GUG...GUG... GARDEN GNOMES...

WHAT'S HE SAYING?

I'M NO GOOD AT THIS...I DON'T HAVE ANY PATTER!

AW! AREN'T THEY SWEET!

I'D LOVE ONE... BUT I'VE NO MONEY!

AND SO....

I COULDN'T SELL THEM... SO I GAVE THEM AWAY!

YOU DID WHAT?

DON'T FUSS! I SOLD THE SUIT-CASE FOR FIVE QUID TO SOME BLOKE...

B...B...BUT...

BUT I KNOW YOU'RE ONLY TRYING TO PROTECT... HIM!!

HONEST FACE... BAH!! HE'S A HOPELESS 'CASE'!

YOU DIMBO! THAT WAS DAD'S BEST GOOTCHY, WASN'T IT?

WHAT? WELL, I DIDN'T KNOW THAT, DID I?

BACK HOME...

I'VE GOT TO COME CLEAN, DAD...IT WAS MY FAULT... I SOLD YOUR SUITCASE!

HMM...IT'S NOT LIKE YOU TO TELL FIBS, RODNEY.

Mr. Hill.

WALT TEASER

ADAM ADMAN

GROAN! WORRY! OH, DEAR...

WHAT'S THE MATTER, ADAM? IS IT THE END OF THE WORLD?

I'VE JUST SEEN AN AD ON TELLY THAT SAYS KIDS CAN HAVE BUILDING SOCIETY ACCOUNTS... AND I HAVEN'T GOT ONE!

SOB! SOB!

SO, OPEN ONE!

BUT I'VE NO MONEY!

YOU COULD EARN SOME MONEY BY HELPING WITH THE HOUSEWORK.

MEGA! I'LL USE THE HYPER-POWER VACUUM CLEANER...AS ADVERTISED ON TV!

I'VE GOT TO GO OUT... SO CAN I TRUST YOU?

OF COURSE YOU CAN, MUM! I'M A RESPONSIBLE PERSON...THAT'S WHY I'M MAKING THIS BIG STEP OF OPENING AN ACCOUNT WITH THE APPLIANCE AND PESTER!

HE'S LIKE A LITTLE OLD MAN SOMETIMES!

VVVAVOOM!

BUT HE IS DOING THE HOUSEWORK!

MINUTES LATER...

SCOOT!

THAT DIDN'T TAKE LONG! NOW FOR THE FIRST STEP IN THE FINANCIAL WORLD!

WOW! THEY GAVE ME A BOOK...AND A CARD...AND A FREE PIGGY BANK. JUST LIKE THOSE KIDS ON THE AD!

YOU LEFT THAT SUPER-POWER VACUUM SWITCHED ON! IT'S SUCKED UP EVERYTHING... FURNITURE, CARPETS, THE HOUSE, THE LOT!

GULP!!

BULGE!

SUCK!

GOOD! SEE IF YOU CAN GET A BIG LOAN FROM THEM!!

EH? WHAT FOR?

-B. GLENNARD-

Mummy's Boy

ONE FOR ALL   ALL FOR ONE   Teachers UNITED